First published in 2007 by Culture and Sport, Glasgow
Book printed and bound by Reid Printers, Blantyre
DVD filmed by ETC media and reproduced by gt4 media
ISBN 978-0-906169-66-7

Rhyme Time

Illustrations by
Mandy Sinclair

Thanks

To all parents, carers and children who took part in the production of
the DVD and to the staff who gave their valuable support and input
in the publishing of this wonderful book and DVD.
Also thanks to Doigs Limited for their generous sponsorship of this book.

Contents

Notes
Demonstration DVD included

Introduction

Bounce and Rhyme Time is a fun activity for parents, carers and children, 0-3 years to enjoy action songs, rhymes and stories together.

This is a fun time to share between adult and child. Singing, reading and talking together can help improve the literacy and numeracy skills of children in their pre-school and school years.

As you sing, repeat rhymes and share stories with your child you help to increase their vocabulary and develop skills which can improve their speech, language and communication.

'Rhyme Time' gives all the words and actions of twenty favourite rhymes. It also contains a DVD that demonstrates the actions to each song whilst being performed by parents, carers and children at Bounce and Rhyme Time in their local library. This will give families an opportunity to learn the actions to enjoy the fun at home.

Eye, nose a cheeky cheeky chin

Eye, nose a cheeky cheeky chin
  Cheeky cheeky chin nose I

*Point to the parts of the face as you
say the rhyme*

Mouse in the House

Round about *(1)*
  Round about
Like a wee mouse
  Up a bit *(2)*
Up a bit
  In a wee house *(3)*

*(1) Draw small circles
on palm of hand
(2) Climb up arm with
fingers
(3) Tickle under arm*

Twinkle, Twinkle Little Star

Twinkle, twinkle little star *(1)*
  How I wonder what you are? *(2)*
Up above the world so high *(3)*
  Like a diamond in the sky *(4)*
Twinkle, twinkle little star *(5)*
  How I wonder what you are *(6)*

(1) Use fingers in twinkle motion
(2) Point finger at self
(3) Point up high
(4) Make diamond shape with fingers
(5) Use fingers in twinkle motion
(6) Point finger at self

Little Peter Rabbit

Little Peter Rabbit had a fly upon his nose *(1), (2)*
  Little Peter Rabbit had a fly upon his nose *(1), (2)*
Little Peter Rabbit had a fly upon his nose *(1), (2)*
  And he flipped it and he flopped it and it flew away *(3), (4)*

Floppy ears and curly whiskers *(5), (6)*
  Floppy ears and curly whiskers *(5), (6)*
Floppy ears and curly whiskers *(5), (6)*
  And he flipped it and he flopped it and it flew away *(7), (8)*

(1) Pretend rabbit ears with hands held to head
(2) Point to nose where fly would be
(3) Swipe at fly with hands
(4) Flap hands to indicate fly flying away
(5) Pretend rabbit ears with hands held to head
(6) Using hands near face pretend to curl
whiskers around fingers
(7) Swipe at fly with hands
(8) Flap hands to indicate fly flying away

Round and Round the Garden

Round and round the garden, *(1)*
  Like a teddy bear
One step, two steps *(2)*
   Tickly under there *(3)*

(1) Circle child's palm with your finger
(2) Walk your finger up child's arm
(3) Tickle child under arm

Incy Wincy Spider

Incy wincy Spider climbing up the spout *(1)*
  Down came the rain and washed poor Incy out *(2)*
Out came the sunshine and dried up all the rain *(3)*
  So Incy Wincy Spider climbed up the spout again *(4)*

*(1) Wriggle fingers of both hands and raise arms slowly,
to represent a climbing spider
(2) Lower arms slowly, moving fingers as if they were raindrops
(3) Open arms wide to represent sunshine
(4) Wriggle fingers of both hands and raise arms slowly,
to represent a climbing spider*

Ally Bally

Ally Bally Ally Bally bee
  Sittin on your mammy's knee *(1)*
Greetin fir a wee bawbee
  To buy some coulters candy

Coulters candy a penny a lump *(2)*
  That's the stuff to make you jump *(2)*
If you jump you're sure to fall *(3)*
  Okey dokey that's it all

Poor wee Jeannie she's affy affy thin
  A bag of bones wrapped in skin *(4)*
Now she's getting a wee double chin *(5)*
  From eating coulters candy

Coulters candy a penny a lump *(2)*
  That's the stuff to make you jump *(2)*
If you jump you're sure to fall *(3)*
  Okey dokey that's it all

(1) Bounce child gently on your lap
(2) Bounce them higher at words jump and lump
(3) Let baby slide through legs at the word fall
(4) Cuddle child and rock
(5) Tickle under child's chin

The Wheels on the Bus

The wheels on the bus go round and round *(1)*
  Round and round, round and round
The wheels on the bus go round and round
  All day long

The wipers on the bus go swish, swish, swish, *(2)*
  Swish, swish, swish, swish, swish, swish
The wipers on the bus go swish, swish, swish,
  All day long

The driver on the bus goes "Toot! Toot! Toot!" *(3)*
  "Toot! Toot! Toot! Toot! Toot! Toot!"
The driver on the bus goes "Toot! Toot! Toot!"
  All day long

The conductor on the bus goes "Hurry along please!" *(4)*
  "Hurry along please! Hurry along please!"
The conductor on the bus goes "Hurry along please!"
  All day long

The mummies on the bus go "Yakkity yak yak!" *(5)*
  "Yakkity yak yak! Yakkity yak yak!"
The mummies on the bus go "Yakkity yak yak!"
  All day long

The Wheels on the Bus (continued)

The children on the bus make TOO MUCH NOISE! *(6)*
 TOO MUCH NOISE! TOO MUCH NOISE!
The children on the bus make TOO MUCH NOISE!
 All day long

The babies on the bus fall fast asleep *(7)*
 Fall fast asleep, fall fast asleep
The babies on the bus fall fast asleep
 All day long

*(1) Bend elbows and, keeping them close to sides,
move arms round as if they were wheels
(2) Hold up hands in front of face, palm outwards.
Sway hands from side to side
(3) Mime pressing horn
(4) Mime conductor guiding passengers along the bus
(5) Open and shut hands, to represent people talking
(6) Put hands over ears, as if hearing too much noise
(7) Pretend to go to sleep*

This Little Piggy

This little piggy went to market *(1)*
  This little piggy stayed at home *(2)*
This little piggy had roast beef *(3)*
  This little piggy had none *(4)*
This little piggy cried "wee-wee-wee, *(5)*
  All the way home" *(6)*

(1) Wiggle thumb
(2) Wiggle first finger
(3) Wiggle middle finger
(4) Wiggle third finger
(5) Clasp pinky finger
(6) Run fingers up arm

Miss Polly had a Dolly

Miss Polly had a dolly, who was sick, sick, sick *(1)*
  So she phoned for a doctor, to come quick, quick, quick *(2)*
The doctor came with, his bag and his hat *(3)*
  And he knocked on the door with a rat-a-tat-tat *(4)*
He looked at the dolly and he shook his head *(5)*
  He said Miss Polly, put her straight to bed *(6)*
I'll write you a letter for a pill, pill, pill *(7)*
  I'll be back in the morning, yes I will, will, will *(8)*

(1) Hold arms as if to rock a baby
(2) Pretend to hold a phone to ear
(3) Hold out hands as if carrying a bag, pat top of head at word hat
(4) Knock onto palm of hand
(5) Hold arms as if to rock a baby whilst looking down at the baby
(6) Wave finger with instruction
(7) Imitate writing on palm of hand
(8) Wave with hand

Wind the Bobbin up

Wind the bobbin up, wind the bobbin up *(1)*
  Pull, pull, clap, clap, clap *(repeat) (2)*
Point to the ceiling *(3)*
  Point to the floor *(4)*
Point to the window *(5)*
  Point to the door *(6)*
Clap your hands together, one, two, three *(7)*
  Lay your hand upon your knee *(8)*

Wind it back again, wind it back again *(1)*
  Pull, pull, clap, clap, clap *(repeat) (2)*
Point to the ceiling *(3)*
  Point to the floor *(4)*
Point to the window *(5)*
  Point to the door *(6)*
Clap your hands together, one, two, three *(7)*
  Lay you hand upon your knee *(8)*

(1) Make winding motions with hand
(2) Pretend to pull elastic
between hands, clap 3 times
(3) Point up to the sky
(4) Point down to the floor
(5) Point at window
(6) Point at door
(7) Clap hands three times
(8) Place hands on knees

One, Two, Three, Four, Five

One, two, three, four, five *(1)*
  Once I caught a fish alive *(2)*
Six, seven, eight, nine, ten *(3)*
  Then I let it go again *(4)*

Why did you let him go?
  Because he bit my finger so *(5)*
Which finger did he bite?
  This little finger on the right *(6)*

(1) Count fingers on one hand
(2) Pretend to catch fish
(3) Count fingers on the other hand
(4) Pretend to throw fish back
(5) Shake the right hand
(6) Hold up the little finger on right hand

Hickory, Dickory, Dock

Hickory, dickory, dock
  The mouse ran up the clock *(1)*
The clock struck one *(2)*
  The mouse ran down *(3)*
  Hickory, dickory, dock

Hickory, dickory, dock
  The mouse ran up the clock *(1)*
The clock struck two *(2)*
  The mouse said boo *(4)*
  Hickory, dickory, dock

Hickory, dickory, dock
  The mouse ran up the clock *(1)*
The clock struck three *(2)*
  The mouse went weee *(5)*
  Hickory, dickory, dock

Hickory, dickory, dock
  The mouse ran up the clock *(1)*
The clock struck four *(2)*
  The mouse said no more *(6)*
  Hickory, dickory, dock

Hickory, dickory, dock
  The mouse ran up the clock *(1)*
The clock struck five *(2)*
  The mouse said bye bye *(7)*
  Hickory, dickory, dock

(1) Run fingers of one hand quickly up child's arm
(2) At each verse increase number of fingers to indicate time
(3) Run fingers down the child's arm
(4) Cover eyes and make "boo" actions
(5) Slide fingers down arm
(6) Shake finger in no action
(7) Wave bye bye

Five Little Ducks

Five little ducks went swimming one day *(1)*
  Over the pond and far away
Mummy duck says "Quack quack, quack quack" *(2)*
  And only four little ducks came back

Four little ducks went swimming one day *(1)*
  Over the pond and far away
Mummy duck says "Quack quack, quack quack" *(2)*
  And only three little ducks came back

Three little ducks went swimming one day *(1)*
  Over the pond and far away
Mummy duck says "Quack quack, quack quack" *(2)*
  And only two little ducks came back

Two little ducks went swimming one day *(1)*
  Over the pond and far away
Mummy duck says "Quack quack, quack quack" *(2)*
  And only one little duck came back

One little duck went swimming one day *(1)*
  Over the pond and far away
Mummy duck says "Quack quack, quack quack" *(2)*
  And no little ducks came swimming back

No little ducks went swimming one day *(1)*
  Over the pond and far away
Daddy duck says "Quack quack, quack quack" *(2)*
  And five little ducks came swimming back

(1) Make wave motion with hand
(2) Separate thumb and fingers in quacking motion
At each verse reduce the number of fingers to indicate number of ducks

Tommy Thumb

Tommy Thumb is up and Tommy Thumb is down *(1)*
  Tommy Thumb is dancing all around the town
Dancing on my shoulders, dancing on my head *(2)*
  Dancing on my knees and tuck him into bed *(4)*

Peter Pointer is up and Peter Pointer is down *(1)*
  Peter Pointer is dancing all around the town
Dancing on my shoulders, dancing on my head *(2)*
  Dancing on my knees and tuck him into bed *(4)*

Mister Middleman is up and Mister Middleman is down *(1)*
  Mister Middleman is dancing all around the town
Dancing on my shoulders, dancing on my head *(2)*
  Dancing on my knees and tuck him into bed *(4)*

Ruby Ring is up and Ruby Ring is down *(1)*
  Ruby Ring is dancing all around the town
Dancing on my shoulders, dancing on my head *(2)*
  Dancing on my knees and tuck him into bed *(4)*

Baby small is up and Baby small is down *(1)*
  Baby small is dancing all around the town
Dancing on my shoulders, dancing on my head *(2)*
  Dancing on my knees and tuck him into bed *(4)*

All my family is up and all my family is down *(3)*
  All my family are dancing all around the town
Dancing on my shoulders, dancing on my head *(2)*
  Dancing on my knees and tuck him into bed *(4)*

(1) Hold up appropriate finger and wriggle
(2) Point to each part of the body
(3) Wriggle all fingers at the same time
(4) Hide hands behind back

Pop a Little Pancake

Pop a little pancake into the pan *(1)*
  Pop a little pancake into the pan
Pop a little pancake into the pan
  That's for my dinner today

Shake a little sugar with a shake, shake, shake *(2)*
  Shake a little sugar with a shake, shake, shake
Shake a little sugar with a shake, shake, shake
  That's for my dinner today

Squeeze a little lemon with a squeeze, squeeze, squeeze *(3)*
  Squeeze a little lemon with a squeeze, squeeze, squeeze
Squeeze a little lemon with a squeeze, squeeze, squeeze
  That's for my dinner today

Toss it in the air up high, high, high *(4)*
  Toss it in the air up high, high, high
Toss it in the air up high, high, high
  That's for my dinner today

Pop it in your mouth with a yum, yum, yum *(5)*
  Pop it in your mouth with a yum, yum, yum
Pop it in your mouth with a yum, yum, yum
  That's for my dinner today

(1) Clap hands in patting motion
(2) Gently shake child
(3) Give a hug to child
(4) Lift child up into air (holding on tightly)
*(5) Open mouth wide, motion with hand putting item in mouth,
then rub tummy*

Head and Shoulders

Head and shoulders, knees and toes, knees and toes
  Head and shoulders, knees and toes, knees and toes
Eyes and ears and mouth and nose
  Head and shoulders, knees and toes, knees and toes!

Touch each part of body as it is mentioned. Repeat saying rhyme faster

Clap, Clap Hands

Clap, clap hands, one, two, three *(1)*
  Put your hands upon your knees *(2)*
Lift them high to touch the sky *(3)*
  Clap, clap hands and away we fly *(4)*

(1) Clap hands
(2) Put hands on knees
(3) Lift hands high
(4) Clap hands, then raise them into the air, flap arms in flying motion

Old MacDonald had a Farm

Old MacDonald had a farm, E-i-e-i-o
  And on that farm he had some cows, E-i-e-i-o
With a moo-moo here
  And a moo-moo there
Here a moo, there a moo
  Everywhere a moo-moo
  Old MacDonald had a farm, E-i-e-i-o

Old MacDonald had a farm, E-i-e-i-o
  And on that farm he had some ducks, E-i-e-i-o
With a quack-quack here
  And a quack-quack there
Here a quack, there a quack
  Everywhere a quack-quack
  Old MacDonald had a farm, E-i-e-i-o

Old MacDonald had a farm, E-i-e-i-o
  And on that farm he had some sheep, E-i-e-i-o
With a baa-baa here
  And a baa-baa there
Here a baa, there a baa
  Everywhere a baa-baa
  Old MacDonald had a farm, E-i-e-i-o

A singing rhyme: each time the verse is sung, a new animal is named and the sound that animal makes is added. Include as many animals as you like.

If you're Happy and you Know it

If you're happy and you know it clap your hands
  If you're happy and you know it clap your hands
If you're happy and you know it and you really want to show it
  If you're happy and you know it clap your hands

If you're happy and you know it nod your head
  If you're happy and you know it nod your head
If you're happy and you know it and you really want to show it
  If you're happy and you know it nod your head

If you're happy and you know it stamp your feet
  If you're happy and you know it stamp your feet
If you're happy and you know it and you really want to show it
  If you're happy and you know it stamp your feet

If you're happy and you know it shout "WE ARE"
  If you're happy and you know it shout "WE ARE"
If you're happy and you know it and you really want to show it
  If you're happy and you know it shout "WE ARE"

Follow actions in each verse